The Usborne
Illustrated
Robin Hood

2

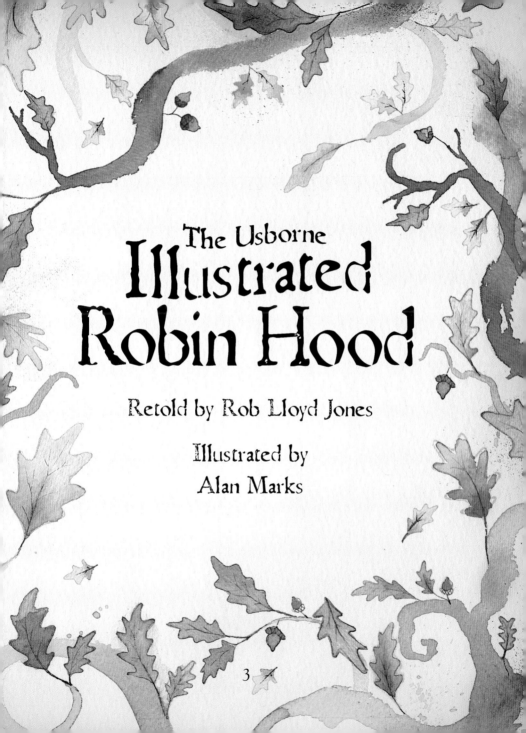

The Usborne
Illustrated
Robin Hood

Retold by Rob Lloyd Jones

Illustrated by
Alan Marks

4

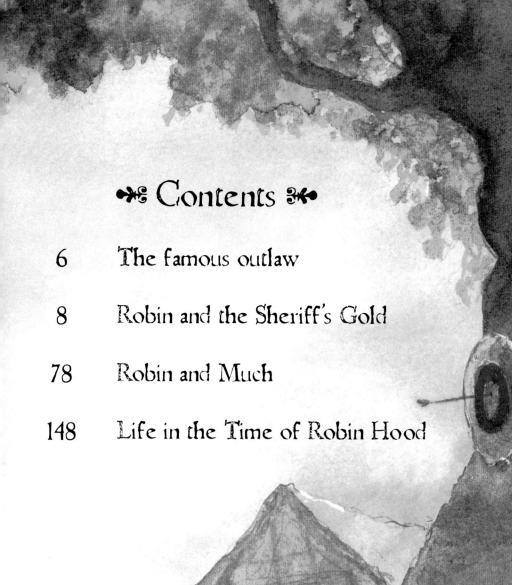

❧ Contents ❧

The famous outlaw

Swashbuckling sword fights, swinging through the trees, secret hideouts... For over 700 years, people have enjoyed stories about Robin Hood – the daring outlaw who robbed from the rich to give to the poor.

Outlaws were runaway criminals – rough, tough, dangerous men. But they were also free, at a time when most people lived under strict laws laid down by the rich.

Some outlaws became heroes because they fought back against corrupt officials, and stories flourished about the particularly courageous Robin Hood. This book tells two of those stories.

Afterwards you can discover more about this famous outlaw and the times he lived in. The question is – was Robin Hood ever real, or are these tales just legends?

8

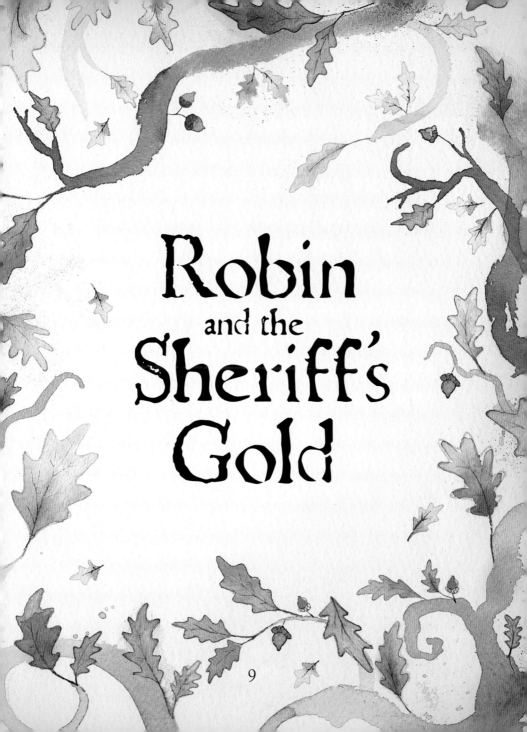

Robin
and the
Sheriff's
Gold

❧ Contents ❧

❧ Chapter 1 ❧

Not just any outlaw

"**P**ay up! Pay up!"
The shrill cry rang out around
Sherwood village. Soldiers marched from
house to house, pounding their fists on
doors and yelling at the villagers.

"Wake up, you stinking peasants!" they
demanded. "Time to pay your taxes!"

Confused villagers stumbled from their homes.
The soldiers rode to Sherwood every month to
collect taxes for the Sheriff of Nottingham, who
owned the land the villagers lived on.

"But we just paid
last week," one of the
villagers protested.

A smug-looking man trotted closer on his horse. It was Guy of Gisborne, the Sheriff's nephew and Chief Guard. "From now on," he declared, "you will pay *every* week."

"But we don't have enough money," the villagers said.

Guy sneered. "Then we'll take whatever you *do* have."

And so the Sheriff's soldiers took all the villagers' valuables – necklaces, brooches, even wedding rings. Guy's bag bulged with loot as he led his troops away through Sherwood Forest. "Uncle *will* be pleased with me," he laughed.

Just then, an arrow whizzed past Guy's face. A shadowy figure appeared high in the branches.

"An outlaw!" Guy shuddered.

"Not just any outlaw," one of the
soldiers yelled. "That's Robin Hood!"

The famous outlaw swung from the trees to the
leafy ground. He gave the soldiers a cheery bow.
"At your service," he said.

"Arrest him!" cried Guy.

Their swords trembled in the soldiers' hands. Robin Hood was not only the most wanted outlaw in England, but also the most dangerous. They'd all heard tales about how fast he was with his bow and arrow, and how skilled with his sword.

Robin strode forward. "You've been stealing from the villagers," he said.

"We can take what we want," Guy snapped. "The Sheriff owns this land."

"No," Robin replied, "the *King* owns this land."

"Ha!" Guy scoffed. "The King is fighting overseas. He will probably never return. Soon the Sheriff of Nottingham will be king. And you, Robin Hood, will be dead!"

Suddenly, Guy lashed out with his sword. The attack caught Robin by surprise, and the tip of Guy's blade sliced the outlaw's hand.

Fast as a flash, Robin Hood leaped back and fired an arrow. It snagged Guy's tunic, pinning him against a tree.

"Help me!" Guy squealed at his soldiers.

But now three more outlaws burst from the bushes. It was Robin's gang. They kicked the soldiers in the shins, stamped on their toes and hit them all on the head.

Robin Hood stepped closer to Guy, his jaw clenched. "Tell the Sheriff," he said, "that as long as he keeps stealing from the villagers, *I* will keep stealing from him."

Guy scrunched his eyes shut in fright. When he finally looked again, Robin Hood was gone. And so was Guy's bag.

Chapter 2

The Sheriff's plan

"Imbecile!"

The cry rang around the walls of Nottingham Castle, followed by a loud crash, as the Sheriff of Nottingham hurled a cup of wine across the hall. The drink splashed all over Guy of Gisborne's terrified face.

"Once again Robin Hood has made a complete fool of you," the Sheriff scoffed, pouring himself another cup of wine.

The Sheriff sighed, stroking his pointy beard. "This outlaw," he muttered, "is like a splinter that I cannot remove."

"I cut his hand, Uncle," Guy spluttered.

"Be quiet!" the Sheriff snapped. "And get up. I have something to show you..."

Guy followed the Sheriff deeper into the castle, down one gloomy passage and then another, until they reached a rusty iron door.

Inside, the room was full of coins. There were bags of glimmering gold coins, boxes of shimmering silver, and piles of pennies all over the stone floor.

"See this money?" the Sheriff boasted, sipping his wine. "This is enough money to make me king. I am certain Robin Hood will try to steal it. Clearly you cannot stop him, Guy."

"I did cut his hand, Uncle..."

"I said be quiet! You are an imbecile. No, I will hold a tournament to find the best fighter in the land. The winner will become my Chief Guard."

"But Uncle," Guy muttered, "I am Chief Guard."

The Sheriff took a sip of wine. Then he hurled the cup at Guy and stormed off.

"Not any more!" he said.

The following day, Robin Hood and his gang held a feast for the villagers at their hideout in Sherwood Forest. Little John cooked rabbit stew, Will Scarlet baked blackberry pies, and Friar Tuck poured everyone a drink.

As the villagers gathered around the crackling fire, Robin gave them back the loot stolen by the Sheriff's men.

Everyone raised their cups, cheering and toasting the famous outlaw. "Good old Robin Hood! He robs from the rich and gives to the poor."

Afterwards there was dancing and singing, as the villagers tried to forget all about the evil Sheriff of Nottingham.

But Robin couldn't forget. He kept thinking about what Guy of Gisborne had said. The Sheriff wanted to become king. It was a chilling thought, but Robin knew it was possible if the Sheriff had enough money.

Robin was desperate to stop him, but how? The Sheriff kept all of his treasure safely guarded in Nottingham Castle.

The villagers spotted Robin looking glum. They danced closer, cheering his name.

"Hooray for Robin Hood!" bellowed one. "He's the best fighter in all of England."

"He should enter the Sheriff's tournament," another of them joked.

Robin looked up, suddenly alert. "What tournament?" he asked.

The villager handed him a poster.

ARE YOU... the best
fighter in England?

PROVE IT... at the
Sheriff of Nottingham's
tournament!

THE WINNER...
will become the new
Chief Guard.

Robin's frown vanished, and a smile spread
slowly across his face. If he won the tournament,
perhaps then he would finally get a chance to
swipe the Sheriff's treasure.

Little John guessed what Robin was thinking.
"You can't enter the tournament," he said. "You'll
be recognized!"

Robin's grin spread wider. His eyes twinkled in
the firelight, as a plan began to form in his head.
"Not necessarily…" he said.

Chapter 3

Tournament day

W ord spread fast about the Sheriff's tournament. Knights rode to Nottingham from all over England, eager to show off their fighting skills. Even the famous Black Knight turned up. Everyone expected him to win.

Excited crowds gathered in the castle courtyard. The Sheriff blew a horn, and the contest began.

The first round was sword fighting. Steel blades clashed and clanged. The crowd cheered louder and louder as the knights battled each other bravely in a ring.

But no one could beat the Black Knight. He was so strong that none of the other knights stood a chance. He stood over the last of them, laughing and jeering at the crowd.

"Who's next?" he yelled.

"I'll try," a voice called.

Everyone turned, as a farmer stepped slowly from the crowd. He had a muddy face and a bushy black beard.

The crowd erupted in mocking laughter. "How can a farmer beat the Black Knight?" someone said. No one knew that the farmer was Robin Hood in disguise.

Robin stepped into the ring, watching his opponent carefully. The Black Knight was very strong, but he wasn't especially fast. Robin knew how to deal with a bully like this.

The duel began, and the crowd fell silent as Robin twisted and turned and ducked and dived, dodging all of the Black Knight's attacks. Suddenly, Robin dropped low and swept away his opponent's legs. With a cry, the Black Knight clattered to the ground.

"The farmer wins the first round!" announced the Sheriff.

"Surely the farmer just got lucky," some of the crowd muttered in disbelief.

Everyone gathered closer as the second round began. This time it was fighting with sticks. Robin and the Black Knight balanced on a log over the castle moat.

"Begin!" yelled the Sheriff.

Clash! Bash! Smack! The sticks crashed together.

Robin ducked one swipe, and dodged another. He needed to attack, but his fake beard slipped on his face. He lowered his stick to straighten it... and the Black Knight seized his chance.

Swinging his stick, he hit Robin into the moat.

"The Black Knight wins the second round!" the Sheriff declared.

It was all down to the archery contest. They each had two shots at the target.

The Black Knight stepped forward to fire first. He drew back his bow and... *Thwack!*

"Bullseye!" he said.

Robin gulped. The Black Knight was very good. He hoped he was better... He breathed in deeply, and fired. *Thwack!*

The crowd gasped in amazement. Robin had hit the bullseye too, only his arrow was closer to the middle.

"Nice shot, farmer," said the Black Knight, with a laugh. "But watch this."

Thwack!

The Black Knight's next arrow hit the target dead in the middle. "There's no way you can win now," he bragged.

"Don't be so sure," Robin thought. He took
another deep, calming breath, and then he fired.
His arrow hit the Black
Knight's – and split
it straight down
the middle!

The crowd went crazy, cheering and clapping.
They had never seen such incredible skill.

Even the Black Knight was impressed. He
grasped Robin's hand and shook it firmly. "You
truly are a champion," he said.

Only the Sheriff of Nottingham wasn't smiling. Barging through the crowds, he dragged Robin away. "Yes, yes," he said, "well done. But now that you are my Chief Guard, there is work to do."

Beneath his fake beard, Robin grinned. He was being led straight into Nottingham Castle. Finally he could get his hands on the Sheriff's treasure.

✤❧ Chapter 4 ❧✤

The treasure room

The door to the treasure room swung open with a rusty creak.

For a long moment, Robin just stared, flabbergasted at the sight of so much gold. He had never seen so much money. There was definitely enough here for the Sheriff to become king.

The Sheriff poked Robin in the chest. "Your job is simple," he said. "I am convinced Robin Hood will try to steal this treasure. So, as my Chief Guard, you must never leave this room."

The Sheriff was right – Robin *was* going to try to steal the treasure. But how? The corridor was guarded by soldiers, and the only window in the treasure room was barely wide enough to fire an arrow through.

To carry the treasure off, Robin needed an excuse to leave the room.

"What if I'm hungry?" he asked.

"Guy will bring you a pie," the Sheriff said.

"What if I need the toilet?"

The Sheriff pointed to a hole in the treasure room wall. "Over there. Now be quiet and start doing your job!"

With that, the Sheriff turned and swept off down the corridor.

As Robin gazed around the room, he suddenly realized how he could steal the treasure. He wrapped a message around an arrow and fired it through the narrow window. He hoped his gang would see the shot from outside.

"Why did you just fire that arrow?" a voice said.

Guy of Gisborne stood in the doorway, holding a steaming pie.

"Just being prepared," Robin replied, casually. "Robin Hood could strike at any moment."

"Ha!" Guy scoffed. "I'm not scared of Robin Hood. I..."

Guy was about to boast that he had cut Robin Hood on the hand. But, as he offered the pie, he saw the very same cut on this farmer's hand.

With a shudder, he realized that this man *was* Robin Hood. Guy decided to remain silent. He would wait until the time was right – and then he would strike.

❖❀ Chapter 5 ❀❖

Thieves in the night

It was the middle of the night. An owl hooted. Moonlight rippled on the castle moat. Three dark figures crept from behind some bushes. Sticking to the shadows, they ran silently towards the castle.

It was Little John, Will Scarlet and Friar Tuck. They had seen Robin's message. It told them to come at midnight and to bring fishing rods. They had a good idea of what he planned...

The three outlaws sneaked right up to the edge of the castle moat. "Quickly," Little John whispered. "We don't have long..."

Quietly, Friar Tuck cast his fishing line into the moat. He wiggled the rod a little, until...

"Got one!" he whispered.

He leaned back, and slowly the line rose from the dark water. Snagged on the end was a bag of jingling coins. It was the Sheriff's treasure.

Now Little John and Will Scarlet cast their lines into the moat as well. In no time they, too, had fished out little bags of the Sheriff's precious gold.

"Here's another," said Little John.

"And here!" added Will Scarlet.

The three outlaws kept fishing, hooking more and more bags of treasure from the bottom of the moat.

"Robin's a genius!" said Little John, impressed with the success of the scheme.

So how did the loot get there?

Up in the Sheriff's castle, Robin Hood couldn't help laughing. Actually, stealing the Sheriff's treasure had been easy. He had simply picked up the bags and dropped them, one by one, into the treasure room's toilet. The bags fell down the long shaft that ran the length of the castle, and splashed into the castle moat below.

Outside, Will Scarlet plucked the last bag from the water. "Let's get out of here," he whispered to the others.

Just as they turned to sneak off, Guy of Gisborne burst from behind a bush. The point of his sword glinted in the moonlight. "You're not going anywhere," he growled.

The outlaws turned to fight, but now a dozen more soldiers emerged from the bushes, spears raised and ready to attack. Robin's gang was outnumbered. They were caught.

Little John dropped his bag of treasure, and smiled at Guy. "You might have caught us," he said, "but you'll never stop Robin Hood."

"Ha," Guy scoffed. "Robin Hood is probably *already* caught."

But Guy was wrong. As he was capturing Robin's gang, more of the Sheriff's soldiers stormed into the treasure room. They searched everywhere. Robin Hood was gone.

The Sheriff was furious when he found out that Robin had escaped. He strode into the castle dungeon, where Little John, Will Scarlet and Friar Tuck were locked in chains.

"Where is Robin Hood?" he demanded. But the outlaws wouldn't say.

"At least you still have your money, Uncle," said Guy. "And all thanks to me."

"Yes, yes," the Sheriff said, "but what about Robin Hood?"

"Surely he will try to rescue his gang," Guy suggested. "And when he does, we'll be ready to catch him."

A cruel smile spread across the Sheriff's face. "Hmm. You may not be such an imbecile after all Guy," he said, storming away. "Hang his gang tomorrow. Let's see if Robin Hood comes..."

Chapter 6

Hanging day

All night, the sounds of hammering and sawing echoed around the Sheriff's castle, as the Sheriff's soldiers built a wooden scaffold in the middle of the courtyard.

Finally, the soldiers lashed three thick ropes around the top of the scaffold – one for each of Robin's gang. This was where the outlaws were going to be hanged.

By morning, dark clouds swirled over Nottingham Castle. Thunder roared in the surly sky.

Villagers gathered in the courtyard, glancing anxiously around the high castle walls. Where was Robin Hood? They prayed that the outlaw would save his friends. But there were so many guards. How could he do it?

A drum roll rumbled around the castle walls. The Sheriff and Guy watched with smug smiles as soldiers marched the prisoners from the dungeon.

Friar Tuck stumbled over, but Little John and Will Scarlet helped him stand. They refused to show the Sheriff that they were scared.

"Long live the King!" Little John bellowed.

"Down with the Sheriff!" yelled Will Scarlet.
"God bless Robin Hood!" Friar Tuck cried.
The crowd cheered, but they were growing
more and more worried by the second. Where
was Robin? He was running out of time to save
his friends…

The soldiers dragged the prisoners up the steps
and onto the scaffold. A hangman looped the
ropes around their necks.

There was another grim drum roll. The Sheriff
gave a signal, and the hangman yanked a lever.

Beneath the prisoners, the scaffold floor swung
away. The three men dangled in the air, struggling
desperately for breath.

The crowd gasped in horror, barely able to
watch. Robin's gang only had seconds left to live...

Another clap of thunder boomed around the courtyard. Lightning streaked across the sky. High on the castle wall appeared an outlaw.

"Robin Hood!" someone cried.

It *was* Robin Hood. But the famous outlaw was too far away. He would never be able to save his friends from there.

Robin drew back his bow and fired a single arrow. It shot over the crowd's heads – and sliced through all three of the hangman's ropes.

Robin's gang tumbled to the ground. They gasped for breath, but they were still alive. Soldiers rushed to grab them, but the villagers surged forward, blocking their path.

The Sheriff's face boiled red with rage. "Forget the prisoners!" he screamed. "Catch Robin Hood!"

Guy of Gisborne led the soldiers up onto the castle wall. They advanced on Robin from both sides. Swords trembled in their hands.

"Surrender!" Guy cried.

"Never!" Robin replied.

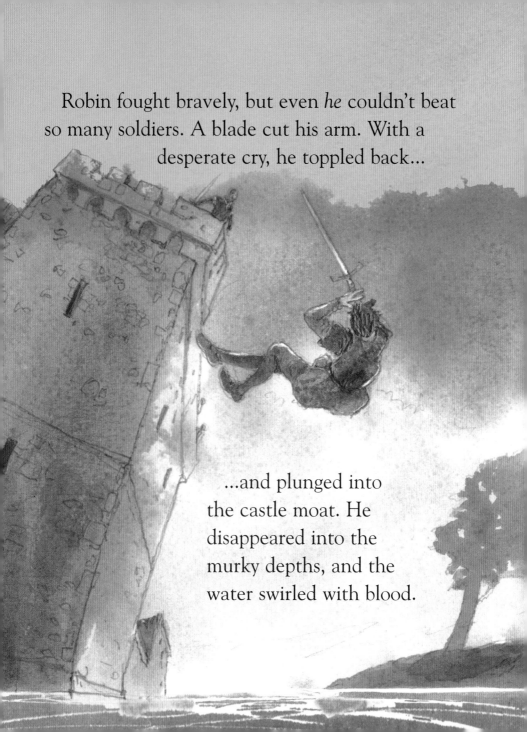

Robin fought bravely, but even *he* couldn't beat
so many soldiers. A blade cut his arm. With a
desperate cry, he toppled back...

...and plunged into
the castle moat. He
disappeared into the
murky depths, and the
water swirled with blood.

Guy, the Sheriff and the soldiers all peered anxiously over the wall, waiting to see if the outlaw rose to the surface. A minute passed. And then another. But Robin didn't rise.

Guy thrust his arms triumphantly into the air. "Robin Hood is dead!" he declared.

But the Sheriff grabbed his collar. "You imbecile," he cried. "Look!"

High at the top of the castle stood Robin Hood. The outlaw had a big grin on his face, and the Sheriff's treasure in his hands.

Guy stared at Robin, then at the moat. He didn't understand. "How... How did he do it?"

Chapter 7

How Robin did it

How did Robin escape? And how did he get the Sheriff's treasure? This is how...

Robin plunged into the castle moat. Blood gushed from his wounded arm as he sank deeper and deeper in the murky water. He was dazed and dizzy, and his mind was spinning. But the icy water quickly snapped him to his senses.

Pain rippled up his injured arm. High above, he saw the blurry shapes of soldiers on the castle wall. If he swam up to the surface, the soldiers would catch him – or kill him. But he was running out of breath...

He thought he would never escape. Then Robin remembered – the castle toilet!

Frantically, he swam along the bottom of the castle wall. Reaching through the murky water, he felt the stone for the hole to the toilet shaft. His lungs burned. His last breath came out as a bubble. And then...

There it was!

Robin burst through the gap and rose, gasping, into the vile shaft.

Groping through the stinking darkness, he managed to wedge himself into the narrow space. The stench made his head spin, but there was no time to stop. Pressing his feet against one wall and his back against the other, he climbed higher and higher up into the castle.

Exhausted, Robin clambered from the toilet shaft and into the Sheriff's treasure room.

The outlaw paused for a moment, still struggling to catch his breath. Just then, a guard attacked, whirling his sword.

Thinking fast, Robin dodged the guard's sword. He snatched a bag of coins and whacked the man on the head, knocking him out cold.

Still, there was no time to rest. This was Robin's only chance to steal the treasure.

He grabbed a larger sack and poured all the gold and silver coins inside. The bag grew heavier and heavier, but Robin made sure he'd swiped every last one of the Sheriff's coins.

When he was finished, the sack was so heavy he could barely lift it. But he didn't need to take it very far.

Groaning with effort, he dragged the hefty sack out of the treasure room, along the corridor, and out onto the sunlit castle wall.

Now Robin had the Sheriff's treasure –
what was he going to do with it? The answer was
obvious. Since the Sheriff had stolen the money
from the villagers in the first place, Robin was
going to give it back.

Raising the heavy sack, the outlaw tipped all
of the treasure down into the castle courtyard.

Gold and silver coins showered all over
the stone ground, scattering everywhere.

"It's all yours," Robin cried. "Don't leave the
Sheriff with a single penny!"

The villagers were delighted. Laughing and
cheering, they rushed around, snatching up
the coins and filling their pockets.

There was much more money than the Sheriff
had taken from them, so from now on the
villagers wouldn't have any problem with paying
their taxes. In fact, they wouldn't have a problem
paying for *anything*.

Of course, the Sheriff was fuming. He grabbed his guards and shoved them towards the villagers. "Stop them!" he cried. "Save my treasure!"

But Robin's gang blocked their way, and the soldiers didn't fight back. They were fed up with working for the greedy Sheriff.

"Imbeciles!" the Sheriff roared. "I'll stop them myself."

But before the Sheriff could draw his sword, Robin fired an arrow. It caught the Sheriff's cloak and pinned him to the wall.

Fast as a flash, Robin fired another shot. This arrow struck the wall inches above the Sheriff's head. A message unrolled from the shaft, and hung right in front of the Sheriff's face...

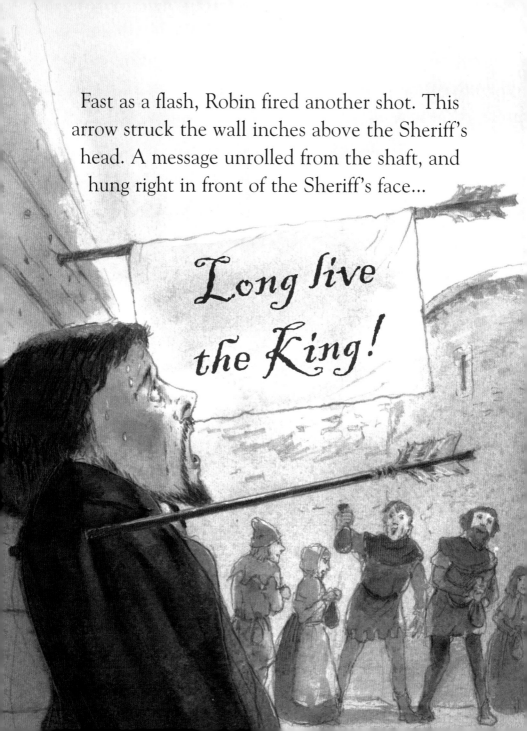

Long live the King!

The Sheriff of Nottingham trembled with rage. "Stop Robin Hood!" he screamed. "Save my treasure!"

But his treasure was gone.
And so was Robin Hood.

Robin and Much

Contents

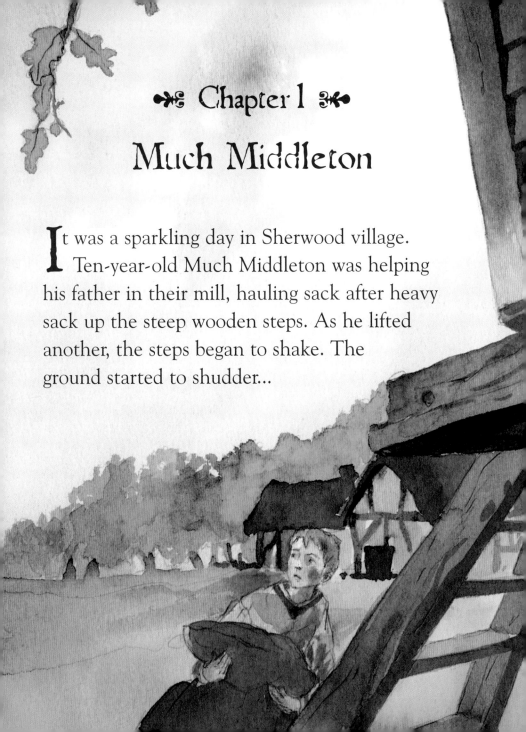

❧ Chapter 1 ☙

Much Middleton

It was a sparkling day in Sherwood village. Ten-year-old Much Middleton was helping his father in their mill, hauling sack after heavy sack up the steep wooden steps. As he lifted another, the steps began to shake. The ground started to shudder...

Swords and spears glinted in the sunlight as a troop of soldiers pounded into the village, led by the Sheriff of Nottingham. Once more, he had appeared in Sherwood to demand money from the villagers.

The Sheriff rode forward, peering down at the villagers as if they were something he'd just picked off his boot.

"All of you peasants have to pay me more taxes," he declared in a snooty voice.

Much's father barged forward. "Only the King can raise taxes," he yelled furiously.

The Sheriff's face twisted into a cruel sneer. "The King is overseas," he said. "*I* am in charge now, and *I* can do whatever I please."

With that, he lashed his reins and charged back to his castle. "I'll be back for my money tomorrow, peasants!" he yelled.

That evening, Much lay in bed watching his father count their money. There wasn't nearly enough to pay the Sheriff his taxes.

"Dad?" he asked sleepily. "Do you think Robin Hood could help us?"

Robin Hood was the mysterious outlaw who stole money from the Sheriff to give to poor villagers. People said he lived in a hideout deep in Sherwood Forest, though Much wasn't sure.

"Well," Much's dad muttered, "we could certainly use his help now..."

Much sat up, his eyes shining with excitement. He adored stories about Robin Hood. "Is it true that Robin once defeated twenty of the Sheriff's men?" he asked.

His dad leaped up, twirling a shovel like a sword. "Fifty!" he joked. "No, a hundred!"

Just then there was a noise outside, like someone tapping on the door. The smile slipped from Much's father's face.

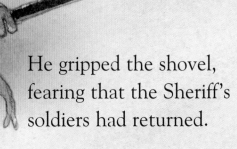

He gripped the shovel, fearing that the Sheriff's soldiers had returned.

Slowly, he crept to the door – and flung it open... but no one was there.

On the door, a velvet pouch swung gently in the evening breeze. Curiously, Much's father took it down and peered inside. It was filled with twinkling golden coins.

More and more villagers emerged from their homes. Every one of them had a pouch of coins on their door too.

"They're from Robin Hood," one of the villagers yelled.

All of the villagers joined in, laughing and cheering in praise of the outlaw. "Hooray for Robin Hood! God bless Robin Hood!"

"Much!" his father called. "You must come quickly and see."

But Much had already seen. He gazed wide-eyed through the window as a shadowy figure leaped across the rooftops to Sherwood Forest.

"Robin Hood," Much gasped.

Chapter 2

On the run

The Sheriff of Nottingham returned to Sherwood the next day, looking forward to arresting a few villagers. When he saw that they had the money to pay their taxes, his face turned red with rage.

"Robin Hood stole that money from me!" he spat. "Because of this, I am doubling taxes again!"

Much trembled with anger. He *despised* the greedy Sheriff. When no one was looking, he scooped up a handful of sloppy horse dung... and hurled it splat into the Sheriff's face.

"God bless Robin Hood!" he cried.

Guards pounced at him, but Much ducked and dived, dodging their grasp. As he fled, his father sprang at the soldiers and wrestled them to the ground.

"Run!" he yelled. "Run, Much!"

Heart pounding, Much ran into the forest and scrambled up a tree to hide. His breaths came in ragged gasps, and tears trickled down his cheeks. His father had been arrested, and it was all his fault.

Much was furious with himself. He *had* to rescue his father, but how?

There was only one person who could help him... Much had to find Robin Hood.

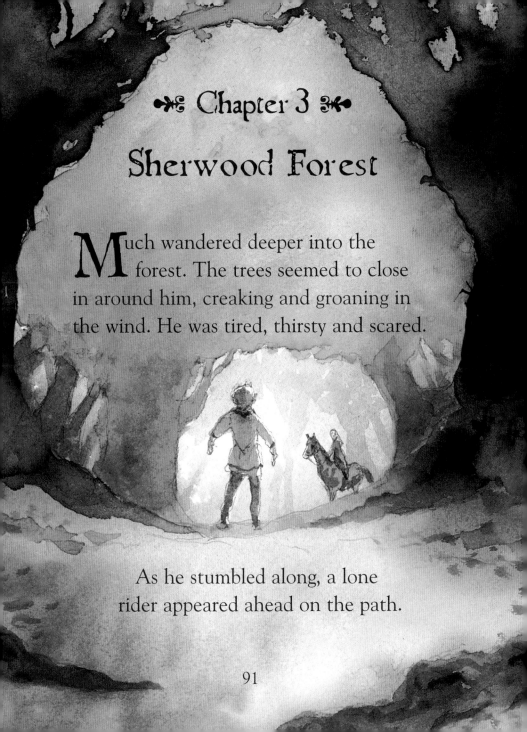

❧ Chapter 3 ❧

Sherwood Forest

Much wandered deeper into the forest. The trees seemed to close in around him, creaking and groaning in the wind. He was tired, thirsty and scared.

As he stumbled along, a lone rider appeared ahead on the path.

A horse trotted closer, carrying a woman dressed in a flowing silk gown and glittering gold necklace.

Much recognized her at once – it was Lady Marian, the King's cousin. Like Robin Hood, Marian often gave money to poor villagers.

"What are you doing out here all alone?" she asked Much.

"I... I'm looking for someone," he replied.

"Let me help you. Climb up."

Much was so exhausted he could barely climb onto the horse. Just as he sat in the saddle, Marian spotted something move in the trees. "Outlaws!" she cried. "Hold on tight!"

She lashed the reins and suddenly they were racing down the path.

High in the forest, several dark figures leaped from tree to tree, chasing Marian and Much.

Marian lashed her reins harder, desperate to escape. "Ya! Ya!" she cried.

93

Marian spurred her horse on, but the outlaws kept up. Much couldn't believe how fast they were. They leaped from one tree, swung from the next, and ran along the branches.

At a crossroads in the woods, Marian yanked the reins, finally stopping the horse. She glanced around, checking if the outlaws were still following. "I think they've gone," she said, sighing with relief.

But she didn't see the face hidden in the tree, or the sneaky hand reaching silently from the low, leafy branches...

Marian screamed in shock. Her necklace had been stolen!

Much spotted one of the outlaws escaping through the woods. "Robin Hood!" he yelled.

Barely thinking, he leaped from Marian's horse and set off after the mysterious figure. "Wait!" he cried. "Is that you Robin Hood? Please wait. I need to talk to you!"

Much raced deeper into the woods. Spiky branches tore his clothes, and thorns cut his skin. But he didn't care – he had to find Robin Hood.

"Robin Hood!" he yelled. "Are you there?" But all Much saw were branches rustling in the wind.

Marian caught up with him, out of breath. "Are you crazy?" she snapped. "Those outlaws are dangerous."

Ignoring her, Much yelled at the top of his lungs, "Robin Hood! I need your help!"

Another rush of wind trembled the trees. High above, four dark figures appeared among the branches, armed with bows and arrows.

"You'd better come with us," one of them called. "Follow the arrows."

Thunk! An arrow thudded into the path in front of Much.

Much climbed back onto Marian's horse
and they set off again, following one arrow...

Thunk!

then another...

Thunk!

and then several more.

Thunk!

Thunk!

They jumped over bushes and rode under
branches, until they reached a clearing deep
in the heart of the forest.

Several small huts sat among a circle of trees, hidden by tangled branches and twisting vines. A fire crackled in the middle, its soft light flickering around the huts' wooden walls.

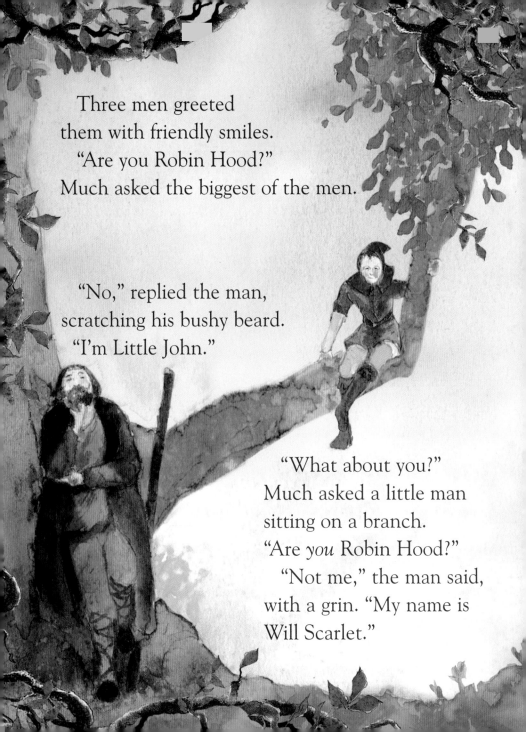

Three men greeted
them with friendly smiles.
"Are you Robin Hood?"
Much asked the biggest of the men.

"No," replied the man,
scratching his bushy beard.
"I'm Little John."

"What about you?"
Much asked a little man
sitting on a branch.
"Are *you* Robin Hood?"
"Not me," the man said,
with a grin. "My name is
Will Scarlet."

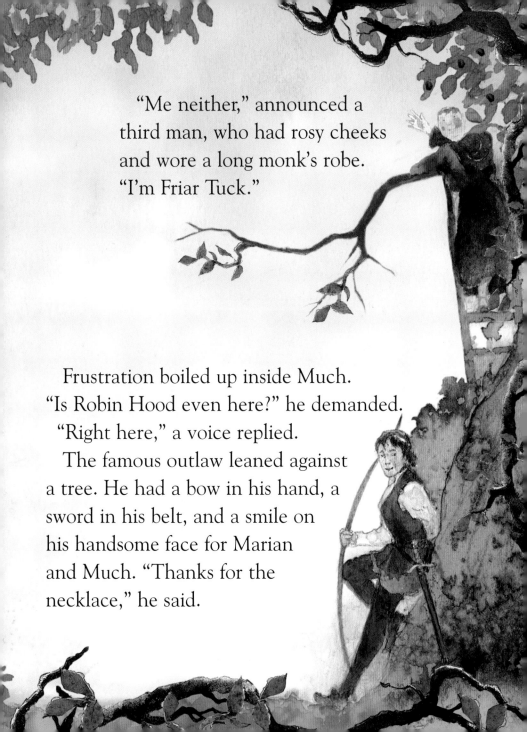

"Me neither," announced a third man, who had rosy cheeks and wore a long monk's robe. "I'm Friar Tuck."

Frustration boiled up inside Much. "Is Robin Hood even here?" he demanded.

"Right here," a voice replied.

The famous outlaw leaned against a tree. He had a bow in his hand, a sword in his belt, and a smile on his handsome face for Marian and Much. "Thanks for the necklace," he said.

Marian didn't find that funny at all. She burst forward, her cheeks flushing red with fury. She looked as if she was going to punch Robin on the nose. "That necklace was a gift from my uncle," she fumed. "Why would *you* want it?"

"He won't keep it," Much explained, putting out an arm to stop her. "Robin Hood gives all his loot to the villagers so they can pay their taxes."

"Really?" Marian asked. Her cheeks turned even redder – this time with embarrassment. "Well, in that case, I suppose you may keep it. I thought you were just a common thief."

"No," said Robin, winking at Much, "I'm a very good thief."

"The Sheriff of Nottingham calls us outlaws," Robin explained. "But *he* is the one breaking the law, every time he raises the villagers' taxes without the King's permission."

"Things are getting worse," Much said. "The rotten Sheriff has doubled our taxes, and now he's arrested my father too. I think he's locked him up in his castle dungeon."

Much expected Robin to leap into action. So he could hardly believe it when the outlaw simply shook his head sadly and walked away.

"I'm sorry," said Robin, "but we can't help your father. The King will free him when he returns. Until then, you're welcome to live with us."

Much sat down alone in the outlaws' hideout, shaking with anger. Robin Hood was supposed to be a hero! Well, Much thought, it didn't matter. He was still determined to rescue his father – with or without Robin Hood.

Chapter 4

Robin and Much

It was midnight in the moonlit hideout. The only sounds were the hoot of an owl and the crack of a twig, as Much crept from a hut, dragging one of the outlaws' heavy swords. If he was going to rescue his father, he'd need a weapon.

"Leaving already?" a voice called. Robin Hood stepped from the shadows.

Much glared at the outlaw. "I'm going to rescue my father," he snapped, "because *you* can't be bothered."

The smile slipped from Robin's face. As he took the sword from Much, his voice turned deadly serious. "I do want to help you," he explained, "but I can't."

"Why not?"

"Come with me and I'll show you."

Reluctantly, Much followed the outlaw from the hideout and through the woods. They jumped from tree to tree, and swung on tangled vines. Soon, they reached the edge of the forest. Sherwood village sat silent and sleepy.

"Why can't you help?" Much whispered.

"You'll see," said Robin, handing Much a jingling pouch of coins. "I stole these from the Sheriff," he added. "Will you help me hand them out to the villagers?"

Much took the coins. He'd help Robin, he decided, and then he'd save his father.

So they split up – sneaking from shadow
to shadow, creeping over rooftops, and slipping
into houses to leave the money.

Much left coins on doorsteps, windowsills and
even under the villagers' pillows. He couldn't help
feeling excited – after all, he was joining Robin
Hood on a thrilling secret mission – but, even so,
he couldn't forget his father.

Afterwards, he sat with Robin on a roof, watching the villagers discover their treasure.

"God bless Robin Hood!" one of them cried with delight. "He's saved us from the Sheriff."

"Now do you see?" said Robin. "This is why we can't rescue your father. The Sheriff's castle is a dangerous place, with dozens of guards. If we get caught, how will the villagers pay their taxes?"

Much gazed up at the Sheriff's castle. In his heart, he knew that Robin was right.

But he had to do *something*. "Then, until my father is free," he declared, "I'll help you protect the villagers."

Robin ruffled Much's hair. "In that case, we'd better teach you a few tricks," he said.

The next day, Friar Tuck cooked a delicious feast for Robin and his gang in their forest hideout. They ate succulent roast deer, bowls of rabbit stew and sticky slabs of blackberry pie.

Afterwards, Will Scarlet taught Much how to fight with a sword. It was hard work, but each time Much got tired, he thought about the greedy Sheriff and he found the energy to continue. Soon Much was ducking and rolling and thrusting and striking.

Will was impressed. "You're a natural outlaw Much," he said.

Next, Little John gave Much a lesson in fighting with a stick. That was even harder for Much, who was barely half Little John's size. But he gritted his teeth and swung his stick, and thwacked Little John on the shin.

"Yow!" howled Little John. "I surrender!"

The next lesson was archery, and this time Much's teacher was Robin Hood.

The bow was almost as big as Much, and the arrows were fiddly to fire. With each shot, though, Much got closer and closer to the bullseye.

THWACK!

THWACK!

THWACK!

But he was never as good as Robin Hood.

Much lived with Robin's gang for weeks. Each day they swung through the forest...

...and crept through the towns. They robbed from the rich...

...and gave to the poor. Much got better and better at being an outlaw.

But the best part of being an outlaw was stealing from the greedy Sheriff. Whenever the Sheriff's soldiers rode through Sherwood Forest carrying tax money, Robin and his gang would never be far off. Much's heart always thumped so hard he was sure it would give him away.

Using crafty disguises and clever hiding places, the outlaws moved through the trees, getting closer and closer to their prey. And then they struck.

Usually, the soldiers didn't even know the tax money had been stolen – at least, not until they saw the teasing messages that Much left for them in their saddle bags.

Much loved being part of Robin's gang. But still he couldn't stop worrying about his father, locked up in the Sheriff's castle. Each day Much wondered when the King would return. He dreamed of the day that his father would finally be freed.

Thanks for
the money!
Robin Hood

Chapter 5

The Sheriff's castle

Lady Marian was growing worried about the King's return too. It had been weeks since her uncle was due home. She decided to ask the Sheriff if he had any news.

As she rode to his castle, Marian shuddered. Even on a sunny day, the Sheriff's home looked grim and gloomy, perched high on its craggy hill.

Inside, the Sheriff greeted her with a curt bow. "My dear, I'm afraid the King is probably dead."

He frowned, but Marian could see the delight in his dark eyes. "And I suppose *you* want to replace him?" she asked, disgusted.

"Who else?" boasted the Sheriff. "I'm the richest man in the country after all."

"You're a crook," Marian said. "Robin Hood will stop you."

The Sheriff sneered at the outlaw's name. "Robin Hood?" he scoffed. "I hardly think so..."

The Sheriff grabbed Marian's arm and dragged her to the next room. Six knights stood by the fire, dressed identically in black tunics. They had snake-like eyes and brutal, broken faces.

Marian's face paled. "The Six Swordsmen," she gasped.

The Six Swordsmen were the most feared fighters in Europe, famous for their cruelty on and off the battlefield.

"They're my new tax collectors," the Sheriff said proudly. "I'd like to see Robin Hood and his pathetic gang stop *them*! In fact, I rather hope they try..."

❧ Chapter 6 ❧

The Swordsmen strike

That same afternoon, while the rest of the gang was off delivering money to the desperate villagers, Robin gave Much another archery lesson at the hideout.

Much's aim was getting better, but he still couldn't quite hit the bullseye on the target.

"Keep trying," Robin urged. "You're getting closer with each shot."

Much groaned in frustration. "I'll never be as good as you," he muttered.

"It's just practice, Much," said Robin. "You'll hit that bullseye soon enough."

Much sighed and lifted his bow. But just as he was about to fire another arrow, a loud cry rang out through the trees.

"Much! Robin!"

Marian came charging into the clearing. She had raced there straight from the Sheriff's castle, riding so fast that she could now barely speak through her ragged breaths.

"Where is the rest of your gang?" she gasped.

"They're in the village," Robin replied, "handing out the Sheriff's money."

A tingle of fear ran down Much's spine. He could tell that something was wrong. "Marian?" he said. "What's happened?"

"It's the Sheriff," Marian said. "He's hired the Six Swordsmen."

Just then, a dark shadow fell over the outlaws' hideout. A plume of smoke rose over the forest. Far off, Much heard shouts and screams, as if a fight was taking place.

"It's coming from the village!" he said.

Robin grabbed his sword. "Quickly!" he said. "We've got to help."

Much couldn't believe his eyes when they reached Sherwood village. All of the houses had been burned to the ground, including his father's mill, and the air was thick with smoke. Villagers sat among the blackened ruins, their heads sunk despairingly in their hands.

"It was the Six Swordsmen," one of them groaned. "We gave them every penny we had, but they still destroyed our homes."

"Where are Will and Tuck and Little John?" demanded Robin.

"They fought bravely," the villager replied, "but they were captured. The Swordsmen took them to the castle."

Robin stared up at the Sheriff's castle, his face darkening. Much had never seen the outlaw look so serious.

"Now it is time to fight back," Robin declared.

"But how?" asked Marian. "There are only three of us, and the Sheriff has a whole army."

Much scrambled onto the remains of his father's mill. "Will you join us?" he called to the villagers. "Will you join Robin Hood?"

The villagers rushed forward, raising weapons to the air. "We will!" they cried as one.

A wide grin spread across Much's face. Now they had an army too.

❧ Chapter 7 ❧
To the castle

In the dead of night, an arrow shot from the forest and swished through the silvery moonlight. A trail of rope uncoiled from the end as the arrow stuck high in the wall of the Sheriff's castle.

Among the trees, Robin pulled the rope tight. The outlaw turned to Much, his jaw tightening. "Are you sure you're ready for this?" he asked.

Much nodded. He'd never been as ready for anything in his life.

Below, Marian and the villagers watched as the pair began to climb the rope to the castle.

"Wait for our signal," Much called.

The rope dug into Much's hands, but he clung on tight and tried not to look at the dizzy drop below. Soon, Robin was helping him onto the moonlit castle wall.

Everything was deadly quiet...

...until a door crashed open and the Six Swordsmen burst out.

"Robin Hood," one of them growled. "We've been expecting you."

Chapter 8

Fight!

Robin Hood drew his swords as the Swordsmen attacked. "Get behind me Much," he cried. The fighting was fast and furious. The Six Swordsmen were so fast their blades were just a blur. But Robin was even faster.

The outlaw twisted and twirled, ducked and dived. He drove the Swordsmen down a spiral staircase and into the castle's great hall.

Thinking fast, Much pushed hard against a statue of the Sheriff.

The statue toppled over...

...and crashed heavily against four of the Swordsmen, knocking them out cold.

But there were two Swordsmen left. They lunged at Much, whirling their swords.

All Much had to defend himself with was his bow and his wits. He fired a single arrow, hoping to catch one of the Swordsmen's tunics. But his aim wasn't quite right, and the arrow whizzed over the Swordsman's shoulder.

Still the Swordsmen advanced. Their grins spread wider across their pale faces.

"We've got you now," one of them hissed.

Much raced across the hall, but he was trapped. His eyes darted around, searching for any escape. Just then, he had an idea. He gave Robin a signal, hoping the outlaw understood.

Then, slowly, he walked backwards, drawing the Swordsmen even closer.

"Come on then!" he said, his voice crackly with fear. "Are you two just going to stand there smiling, or are you going to fight?"

Much's heart pounded as
the Swordsmen stalked closer.
But his plan was working...

As the two Swordsmen
approached, they didn't spot
Robin Hood climbing the
castle wall...

Above, Robin
clambered up
onto the balcony.

The outlaw waited as Much
led the Swordsmen deeper into
his trap. Robin was amazed
by Much's courage. The Six
Swordsmen were the most
feared warriors in England,
and Much was simply teasing
them. Robin just hoped his
plan would work.

He breathed in deeply. Then
he leaped from the balcony and
grabbed hold of the chandelier.

Swinging on the chandelier, the outlaw crashed into the last two Swordsmen and sent them flying across the hall.

Much couldn't help cheering, but Robin wasn't ready to celebrate yet. "Come on!" he yelled. "We have to find the prisoners before the rest of the Sheriff's guards hear."

Robin and Much raced down the castle stairs, but they were too late. Dozens of soldiers surrounded them, swords drawn and ready to fight. The Sheriff stood by with a smug grin. "There are too many of us," he scoffed. "Even for the two of you."

Much smiled. "Ah," he said, "but there are not just two of us..."

Spinning around, Much fired a single arrow. It whizzed over the soliders' heads and through the castle entrance. A perfect shot.

"Bullseye, Much!" Robin cried.

At Much's signal, Marian and the villagers stormed inside. A huge battle began.

As the battle raged, Marian led Much down to the castle's dark dungeon. Much's heart leaped when he saw his father locked in chains with Little John, Will Scarlet and Friar Tuck.

They grabbed the keys from a hook and released the prisoners. Much's father scooped him up in a big hug, but there was no time to hang around.

"Quick!" Much said. "We have to help the others."

They raced back to the main hall, but the fight was already over. Only the Sheriff refused to surrender. His sword trembled as he waggled it feebly at Robin Hood.

"You can't stop me," the Sheriff snarled. "The King is dead!"

"Really?" a voice boomed from the castle entrance. "I feel quite alive."

The King strode into the hall.

Marian threw her arms around him. "You're back!" she said, crying with joy.

The Sheriff's mouth cracked open and a tiny squeal came out. His sword clattered to the floor as he fled in panic for the castle gate.

As he passed, Much stuck out a leg. The Sheriff tripped and tumbled screaming down the stairs – straight into the castle dungeon.

Little John slammed the door, and Will Scarlet turned the key. Then they raced up the stairs and bowed to the King.

But the King insisted that they did not bow. "It is I who should bow to you," he told Robin and his gang. "I owe you all a huge debt. If you wish, I will make you all knights. You can have everything the Sheriff owned, and live together in this castle."

"Thank you sir," Robin said. "But you should give whatever the Sheriff owned to the villagers. He stole it all from them, after all. Besides, we would have no use for this castle, sir. The forest is our home."

Robin turned to Much. "You can come with us too if you like," the outlaw said.

Much shook his head. He'd loved his time as an outlaw, but it was over now. "My home is the village," he said, turning to give his father a fierce hug.

Robin smiled. He handed Much a sword. "Keep this then, to remember us by."

With that, Robin Hood and his men were gone, swinging silently into the moonlit forest.

"Do you think we'll ever see them again?" Much asked.

"I'm sure we will," the King replied, "whenever we need their help."

And so, Much Middleton's life returned almost to normal. The King had all of the villagers' homes rebuilt, including the mill, and Much went back to working with his father.

One thing was different, though – now Much's father asked *him* for stories about Robin Hood.

148

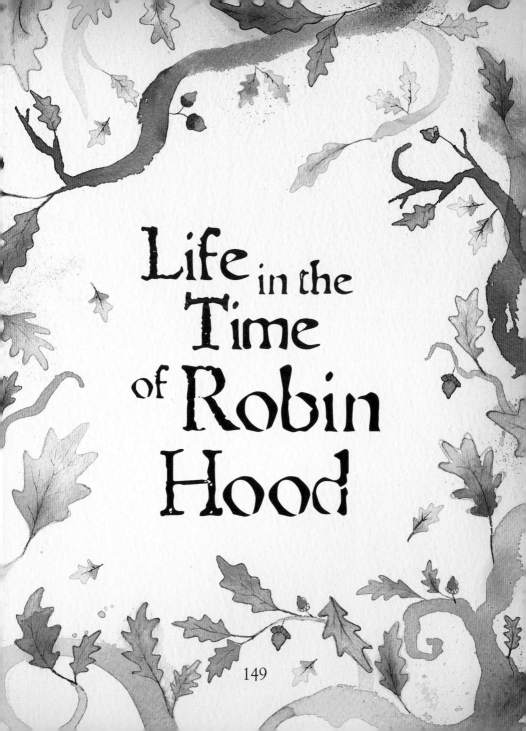

Life in the Time of Robin Hood

Who was Robin Hood?

Stories of Robin Hood have thrilled people for centuries. But did the famous outlaw actually exist? No one can say. The stories are set some time in the late Middle Ages (around 1000-1400) when the name Robin Hood was popular, so there were hundreds of Robin Hoods around. Documents from 700 years ago show that some of these men were accused of crimes. One criminal, named Robert Hood (rather than Robin), was even declared an outlaw in the year 1225. Could he have become the famous Robin Hood?

Unfortunately, there's not much evidence to study about Robin. Early stories of the outlaw weren't written down – they were spoken, or sung in ballads. Over the centuries, they changed a lot.

It's possible that Robin Hood was based on a real person with a different name entirely. The outlaw Hereward the Wake led a rebellion against the English king during the Middle Ages. Was he the inspiration behind tales of Robin Hood?

Hereward
the Wake

Differing accounts

Another reason that it's hard to tell if Robin Hood was a real person is that he's described so differently from one story to another.

Some tales claim that the famous outlaw was once a wealthy lord, whose lands were stolen by the scheming Sheriff of Nottingham. In others, Robin is described as a poor villager who was cruelly treated by the Sheriff's soldiers.

The stories about Robin don't even agree *where* he lived. Most of them say his hideout was in Sherwood Forest, near Nottingham in the middle of England. But in a few, his home is further north, near to the city of York.

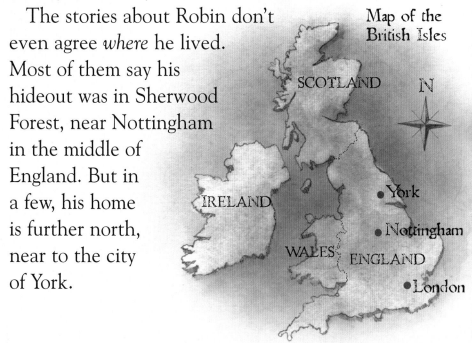

Map of the British Isles

SCOTLAND

N

IRELAND

York

Nottingham

WALES

ENGLAND

London

Robin's first appearance

The first known mention of the hero is in a popular ballad from the 1300s. In the ballad – *Piers Plowman* – a priest says that he knows 'rhymes of Robin Hood'. And, by the end of the 1400s, Robin Hood had become a popular character throughout England.

People dressed up as the outlaw at festivals, and collected money to give to the poor. By then, *who* Robin Hood was didn't really matter. What mattered was *what* Robin was – a defender of the poor, and a hero for everyone.

Singing a ballad

What were the outlaws really like?

If Robin Hood did exist, then he probably wouldn't have been much of a hero at all.

Most outlaws wouldn't have been bothered by anything so noble as robbing from the rich to give to the poor. They were desperate, dangerous men, who stole simply to survive rather than to help others.

An outlaw in the Middle Ages was someone who was accused of a crime, but who fled before a court decided if he was guilty. This person was declared to be **out**side the **law**, meaning that he was no longer protected by England's laws.

Outlaws lost everything they owned and a reward was put on their heads that anyone could claim by catching or killing them. The reward was five shillings – the same as for killing a wolf. So outlaws were nicknamed *wolf's heads*.

Putting up a 'wanted'
poster to catch an outlaw

Like wolves, outlaws were hunted as wild
animals. Most of them spent their lives on the
run – stealing to survive, and praying they'd
never be caught. Only a few of these criminals
were lucky enough to be granted Royal Pardons,
where the king declared they were no longer
outlaws and were free to return home.

An outlaw's life was spent mostly in hiding, and forests made perfect hiding places.

In the Middle Ages, most of England's forests were much bigger than they are now. They were wild, sprawling places of heaths, bogs and dense, dark woodland. An outlaw could easily disappear among the gnarly old oak trees, twisting brambles, or thick banks of fern.

Like Robin Hood, outlaws did steal from the rich, but only because the rich had more to steal.

Wealthy merchants rode through the woods, passing between villages along twisting forest trails. These men were perfect prey for thieves.

Outlaws hid among the trees, lying in ambush, watching, waiting… and then they struck.

Most outlaws wouldn't have thought twice about attacking a man and then leaving him to die among the trees.

Ambushing a rich merchant in a forest

Forests provided outlaws with all they needed to survive. For food, they hunted deer and wild boar that roamed the woods. They stole crops from fields, foraged for nuts and berries among the woodland, and drank from forest streams.

The trees also provided wood for fires and to build huts to protect themselves against the long, harsh English winters.

Sherwood Forest, Robin's home in many stories, was one of the biggest woodlands in England. It was a Royal Forest and belonged to the king. Anyone who hunted there or even collected firewood, without the king's permission, did so illegally. This was called poaching – and if you were caught, you'd be hanged.

Poor villagers, who often struggled to feed their own families, hated the law against poaching. So outlaws who poached often had their sympathy, or even admiration. This is one of the reasons why stories about Robin Hood became so popular.

What was life like for the poor?

For many poor people in the Middle Ages, life was one long struggle. Often they toiled for backbreaking hours in the sizzling summer sun or freezing rain, just to scrape a miserable living.

Few of these people, called peasants, owned their own land. Most of them rented it from a local noble (a rich man with a title). In exchange they paid the noble taxes, and worked on his land too. As if that wasn't enough, they also gave a tenth of everything they farmed to the Church.

Most peasants lived in small villages surrounded by forests and farmland. Some of the villagers had particular skills, such as the blacksmith, or the miller who ground grain in the local windmill. These people could even become wealthy, and live quite comfortably.

But for others life was desperately hard. Their homes were grim cottages that were dark, damp, smoky and smelly. They ate poorly, had no education, and often died very young from disease. Few of them had much chance of ever improving their lives.

As they huddled around fires at night, listening to tales of Robin Hood, some villagers probably dreamed of becoming outlaws themselves – of stealing from nobles rather than paying them taxes, and of feeding their families off the king's precious deer from a nearby forest.

The life of an outlaw, free and wild in the woods, must have seemed very appealing…

Fireside stories of Robin Hood

What was life like for the rich?

A manor house

Wealthy nobles had things much easier. These were rich men with titles such as 'Duke' or 'Lord'. They were given their land by the king in return for their loyalty and help in battles.

Some nobles lived in huge castles with thick stone walls for protection. Others had grand moated mansions, called manor houses, with dozens of servants, and pantries packed with food.

The Sheriff of Nottingham, Robin Hood's enemy, was an especially powerful noble. Sheriffs were men chosen to represent the king in England's shires (counties). They were in charge of collecting taxes and enforcing new laws.

Sheriffs had their own armies of soldiers, who often treated poor people very cruelly. It was also their job to catch criminals such as thieves. That's why the Sheriff of Nottingham is always chasing after Robin Hood.

At the top of English society was the king. In most stories, Robin Hood is fiercely loyal to a king, but it's never clear *which* king.

Some people think Robin lived during the reign of King Richard I (1157 to 1199), who was known as Richard the Lionheart. King Richard didn't spend much time in England – he was always fighting wars.

Richard the Lionheart

When the king was away, greedy nobles often tried to increase their own power, or even become king themselves. If they succeeded, they would be richer than ever. But if they failed, they faced the same fate as any common outlaw – execution.

Violent times

The Middle Ages was a rough time to live. Things that seem cruel to us would have been normal to people then – especially the brutal punishments that were routinely dished out to criminals.

Any outlaw unlucky enough to get caught would almost certainly have been sentenced to death.

Usually they were dragged to public squares, as crowds gathered to watch their execution. Soldiers marched them up onto gallows and they ended their lives swinging on a hangman's rope.

Less serious crimes were punished harshly too. Pickpockets might be flogged, and someone caught lying could be locked in a wooden frame, known as a pillory (if they were standing up), or the stocks (if they were sitting down). They were then pelted with rotten fruit or vegetables by anyone who passed by.

Punishment in a pillory

Punishments like these provided grisly entertainment for crowds. But they were also a warning to anyone among them who might be tempted to turn against the law.

In such violent times, most men knew how to use some sort of weapon – from quarterstaffs (fighting-sticks) to hefty double-edged swords, or the long pikes (spears) carried by a Sheriff's soldiers.

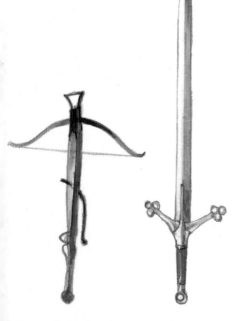

Crossbow   Sword   Longbow   Quarterstaff   Pike

By far the most common weapon in England was the longbow. Made of yew wood, these tall bows fired arrows up to 180m (200 yards).

Back then, archers were the most deadly soldiers in an army. Hundreds of archers could fire at once, raining clouds of arrows over enemy troops. The best archers could fire twelve arrows in a minute.

To show off their skills, archers entered tournaments put on by nobles in the grounds of their castles. The very best shots, like Robin Hood, were admired all over England.

An organized society

English society in the Middle Ages was very well ordered.

The king was the most powerful person in the country. He owned most of England, but gave big chunks of land to nobles in exchange for their loyalty – and their soldiers. Nobles had armies, which the king relied on to support him in war.

The nobles, in turn, gave some of their land to the knights who made up their armies. The knights then gave small strips of land to peasants, who did all the farming.

This system, known as the 'feudal system', meant everyone relied on everyone else and they all owed each other something. Each person knew his or her place – and it was very hard to change it. For centuries, the rich stayed rich, and the poor stayed poor.

Who was who in the Middle Ages

The king
Powerful, but relied on the support of nobles, who often schemed against him.

Nobles
Rich people with lots of land. The Sheriff of Nottingham was a noble, and so was Lady Marian.

Knight
Called 'Sir' – skilled warriors who fought in battles. Sir Guy of Gisbourne was a knight.

Peasants
Poor farmers. The villagers of Sherwood, including Much and his father, were all peasants.

The church
Employed many people, such as priests, monks and nuns. Friar Tuck was a monk.

Robin and his gang

Robin would never have been able to defeat the Sheriff without the help of his friends: a loyal band of outlaws often known as the Merry Men.

The name didn't mean that they were always happy. A 'merry man' was someone who followed a leader, as the outlaws followed Robin.

Little John - who was *not* little. In fact, he was huge. This burly outlaw, whose real name was John Little, was always ready to defend Robin with powerful whacks from his quarterstaff.

172

Will Scarlet - who was known as Will Scathlock in some stories. This name meant 'lock smasher' so, as well as being a skilled swordsman, he was probably an expert thief.

Friar Tuck - a friar was a religious man who visited villages to teach the Bible. Friars wore robes held up by rope-belts, or 'tucks'. This is probably where Friar Tuck's name came from.

Lady Marian - unlike most noble women, who lived quietly in their homes, Marian was feisty and independent. Some stories say that she married Robin, and lived in the forest with him.

❧ Usborne Quicklinks ❧

For links to websites where you can
find out more about Robin Hood,
go to the Usborne Quicklinks Website
at **www.usborne-quicklinks.com** and
type in the keywords "Robin Hood".

Here are some of the things you can
do at the recommended websites:

* Take a photo tour of places where Robin
Hood and his gang may have lived.

* Learn how to use a longbow.

* Visit Sherwood Forest today.

* Explore a noble's manor house
from the Middle Ages.

* Read part of a ballad about Robin Hood,
written around 600 years ago.

Internet Guidelines

The recommended websites are regularly reviewed and updated but, please note, Usborne Publishing is not responsible for the content of any website other than its own. We recommend that children are supervised while using the internet.

Edited by Lesley Sims
Designed by Michelle Lawrence
Digital manipulation by Nick Wakeford
Additional design by Louise Flutter

First published in 2011 by Usborne Publishing Ltd, 83-85 Saffron Hill, London EC1N 8RT, England. www.usborne.com Copyright © 2011 Usborne Publishing Ltd. The name Usborne and the devices ⓠ ⓔ are Trade Marks of Usborne Publishing Ltd.
First published in America in 2011. U.E.